Stereophonics

Just Enough Education to Perform

Universal Music Publishing

Guitar Tablature Explained

Guitar music can be notated three different ways: on a musical stave, in tablature, and in rhythm slashes

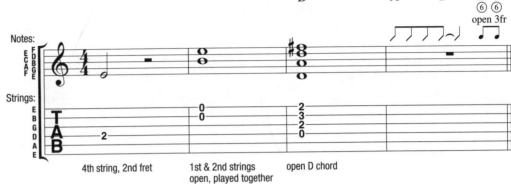

RHYTHM SLASHES are written above the stave. Strum chords in the rhythm indicated. Round noteheads indicate single notes.

THE MUSICAL STAVE shows pitches and rhythms and is divided by lines into bars. Pitches are named after the first seven letters of the alphabet.

TABLATURE graphically represents the guitar fingerboard. Each horizontal line represents a string, and each number represents a fret.

4th string, 2nd fret

1st & 2nd strings open, played together

open D chord

definitions for special guitar notation

SEMI-TONE BEND: Strike the note and bend up a semi-tone (1/2 step).

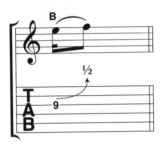

WHOLE-TONE BEND: Strike the note and bend up a whole-tone (whole step).

GRACE NOTE BEND: Strike the note and bend as indicated. Play the first note as quickly as possible.

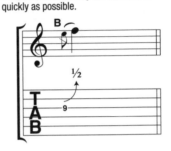

QUARTER-TONE BEND: Strike the note and bend up a 1/4 step.

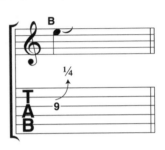

BEND & RELEASE: Strike the note and bend up as indicated, then release back to the original note.

BEND & RESTRIKE: Strike the note and bend as indicated then restrike the string where the symbol occurs.

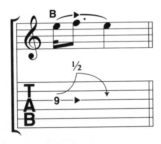

PRE-BEND: Bend the note as indicated, then strike it.

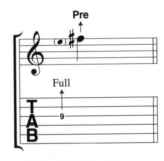

PRE-BEND & RELEASE: Bend the note as indicated. Strike it and release the note back to the original pitch.

HAMMER-ON: Strike the first (lower) note with one finger, then sound the higher note (on the same string) with another finger by fretting it without picking.

PULL-OFF: Place both fingers on the notes to be sounded. Strike the first note and without picking, pull the finger off to sound the second (lower) note.

LEGATO SLIDE (GLISS): Strike the first note and then slide the same fret-hand finger up or down to the second note. The second note is not struck.

SHIFT SLIDE (GLISS & RESTRIKE): Same as legato slide, except the second note is struck.

NATURAL HARMONIC: Strike the note while the fret-hand lightly touches the string directly over the fret indicated.

PICK SCRAPE: The edge of the pick is rubbed down (or up) the string, producing a scratchy sound.

PALM MUTING: The note is partially muted by the pick hand lightly touching the string(s) just before the bridge.

MUFFLED STRINGS: A percussive sound is produced by laying the fret hand across the string(s) without depressing, and striking them with the pick hand.

NOTE: The speed of any bend is indicated by the music notation and tempo.

2

Vegas Two Times

Words & Music by Kelly Jones

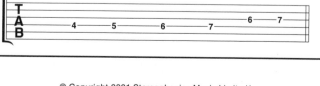

Verse

Chorus

leav - ing L. A. S. Ve - gas two times. Cra - zy Horse to spent us dry. Vi - et - nam vet tax - i ride, L. A. S. Ve - gas.

5

2.

G^7

L. A. S. Ve - gas.

Gtr. 1 w/wah
Gtr. 2 w/Fig. 2

P.M.

P.M.

Bridge

D

Gtr. 3 (acous.)

D^7

$G add^9/D$

mp Gtr. 2 w/Fig. 2

$Gm add^9/D$

D

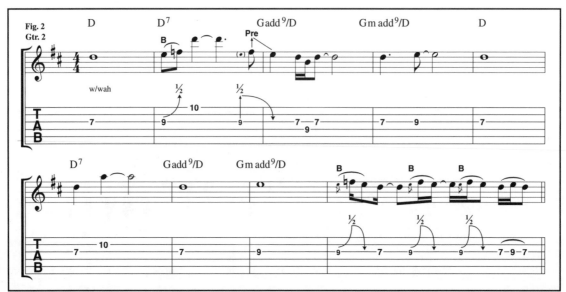

Fig. 2
Gtr. 2

D

D^7

$G add^9/D$

$Gm add^9/D$

D

B

Pre

w/wah

½   ½

D^7

$G add^9/D$

$Gm add^9/D$

B   B   B

½   ½   ½

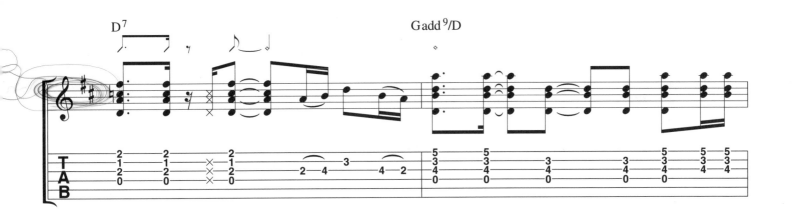

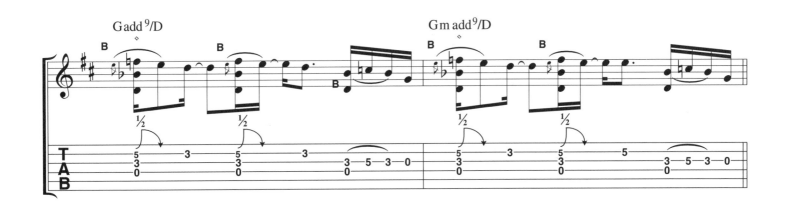

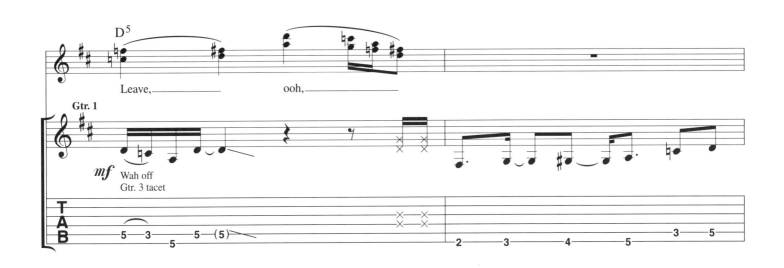

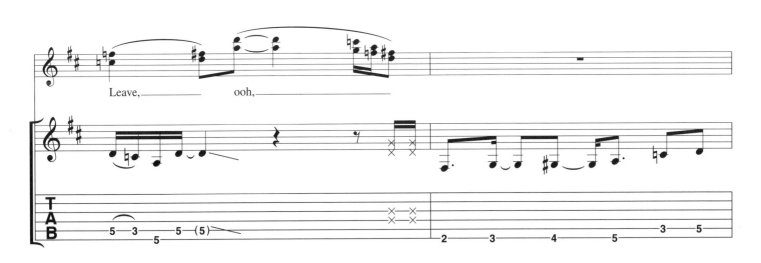

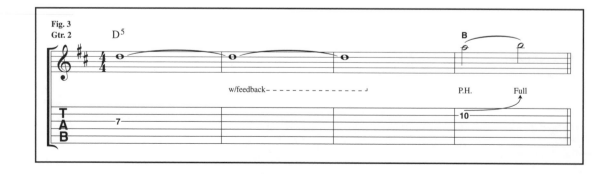

Vi - et - nam — vet tax - i — ride, —

Cra - zy — Horse — too spent us — dry. —

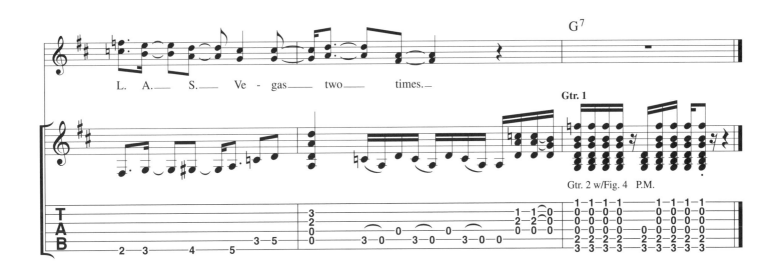

L. A. S. Ve - gas — two — times. —

G⁷

Gtr. 1

Gtr. 2 w/Fig. 4 P.M.

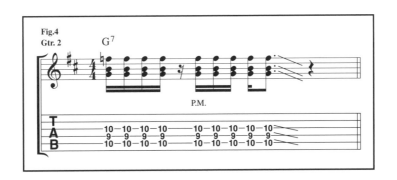

Fig.4
Gtr. 2

G⁷

P.M.

Lying In The Sun

Words & Music by Kelly Jones

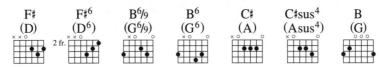

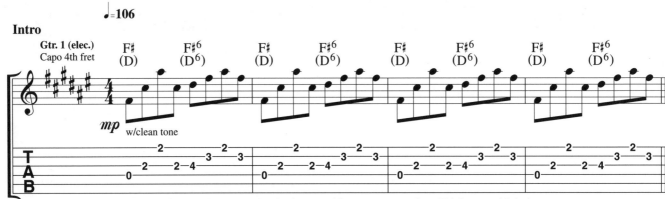

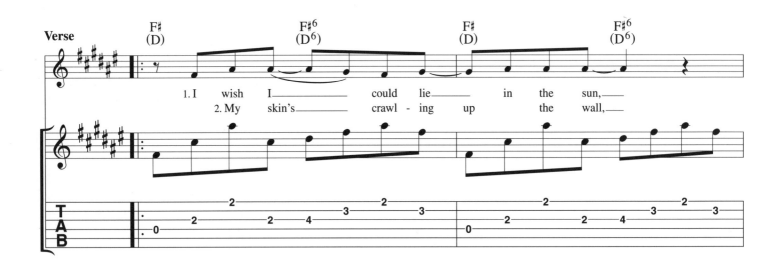

*Symbols in parentheses represent chord names with respect to capoed gtr. (Tab 0 = capo 4th fret)
Symbols above represent actual sounding chords

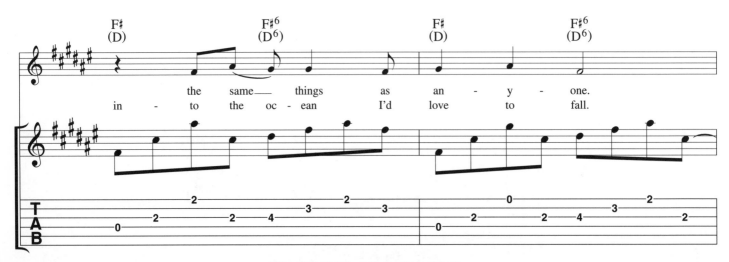

11

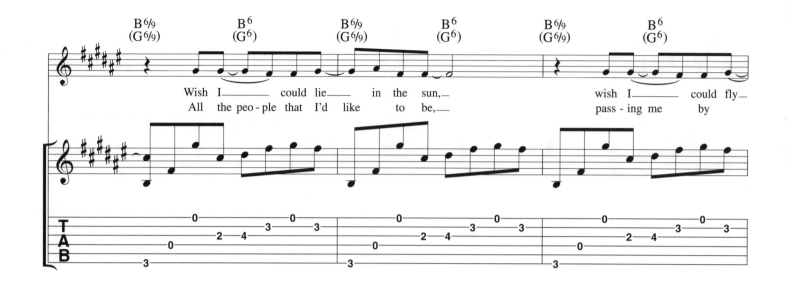

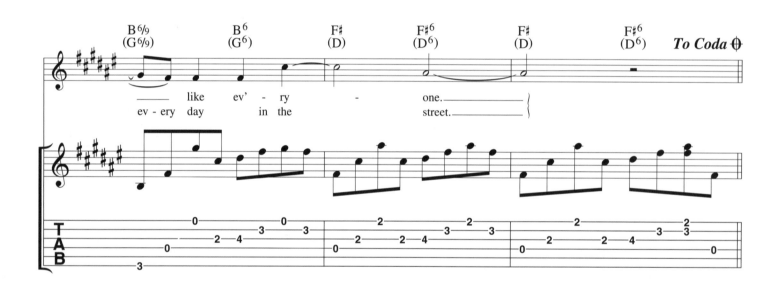

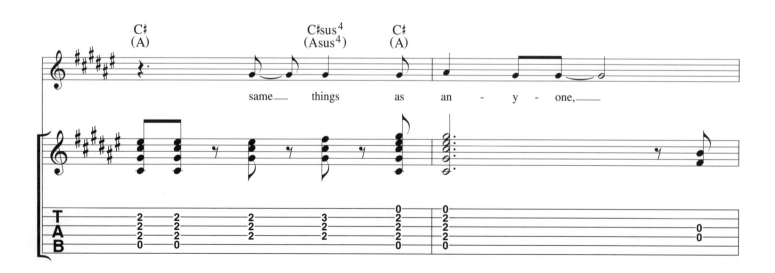

Chorus

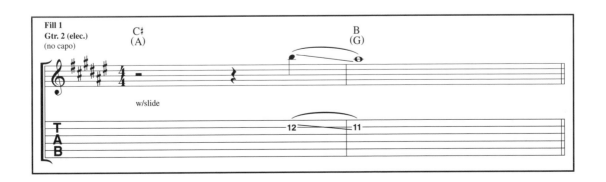

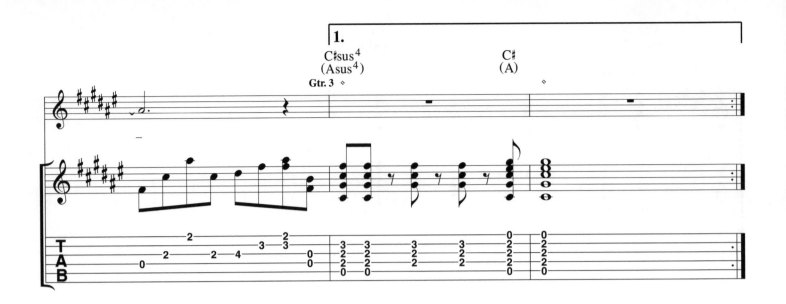

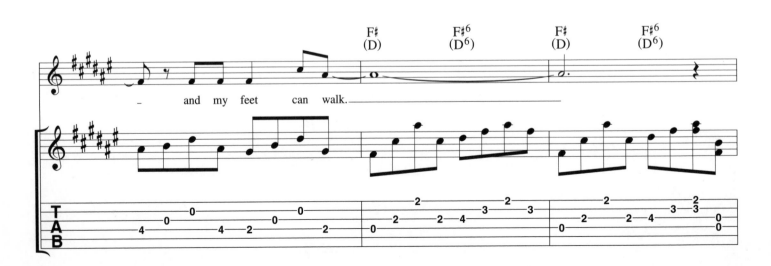

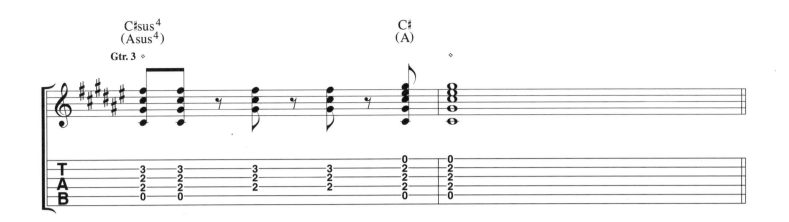

Bridge

Verse 3:
And here I am in the shade on the street
Asking people for money to eat
What did I ever do to deserve this?
Did I kill a child or something worse?

Mr. Writer

Words & Music by Kelly Jones & Marshall Bird

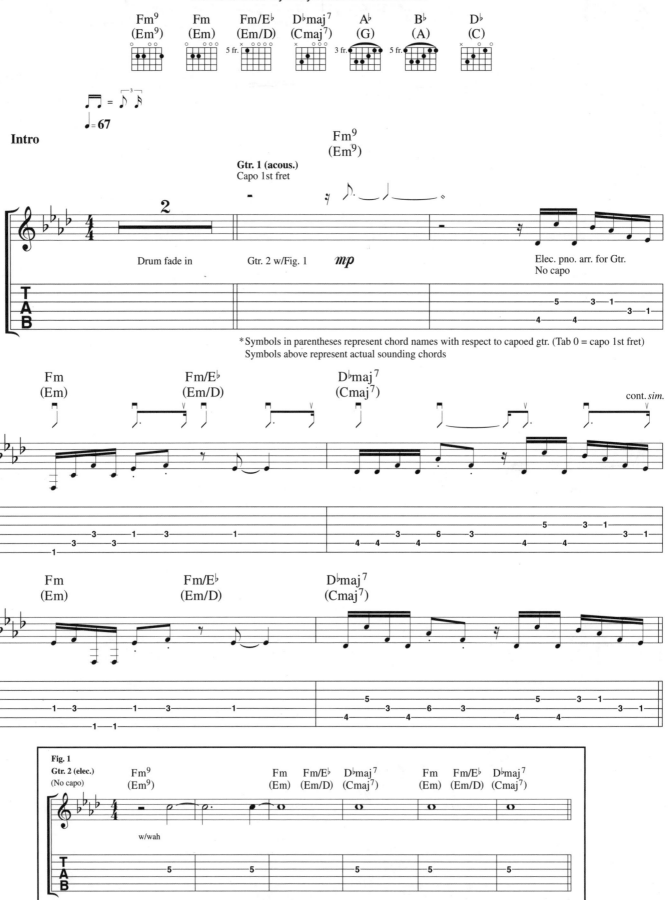

Verse

Lyrics (line 1):
1. You line 'em up,___ look at your shoes,___ you hang names on your wall,___
2. I used to treat you right,___ give you my time, but when I turned my back on___

Lyrics (line 2):
— and you___ shoot them all.___
you, then you___ do what you want.

2° Gtr. 2 w/Fig. 3

Lyrics (line 3):
You fly a-round in planes___ that bring you down___ to meet me, who loves
You've just enough in my own view___ education to perform.

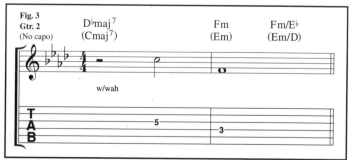

Fig. 3
Gtr. 2
(No capo)

D♭maj7
(Cmaj7)

Fm
(Em)

Fm/E♭
(Em/D)

w/wah

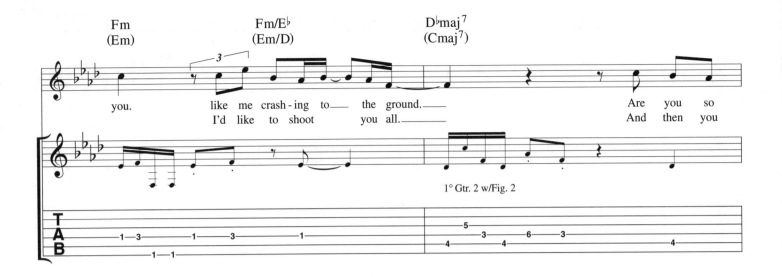

Fm   Fm/E♭   D♭maj7
(Em)   (Em/D)   (Cmaj7)

you.   like me crash-ing to— the ground.—   Are you so
            I'd like to shoot   you all.—   And then you

1° Gtr. 2 w/Fig. 2

Fm/E♭   D♭maj7   Fm/E♭
(Em/D)   (Cmaj7)   (Em/D)

lone - ly?   You don't ev-en   know   me,   but you'd like   to   stone   me.—
go home   with   you   on   your   own,   what do you { really } know?—
                                                              { even }

Gtr. 3 (elec.)
(No capo)

2° (𝄋) Gtr. 4 w/Fig. 4   cont. sim.   w/dist.

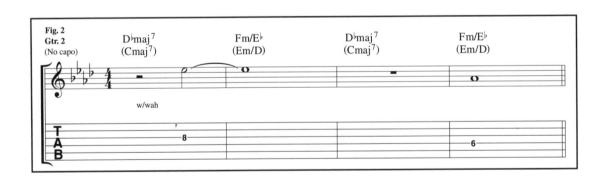

Fig. 2
Gtr. 2
(No capo)   D♭maj7   Fm/E♭   D♭maj7   Fm/E♭
                 (Cmaj7)   (Em/D)   (Cmaj7)   (Em/D)

w/wah

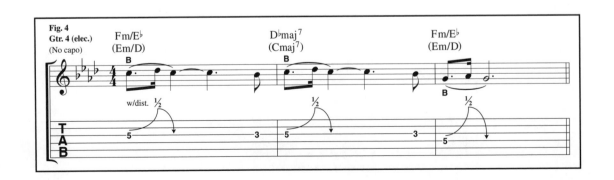

Fig. 4
Gtr. 4 (elec.)
(No capo)   Fm/E♭   D♭maj7   Fm/E♭
             (Em/D)   (Cmaj7)   (Em/D)

w/dist. ½   ½   ½

20

Chorus

Mis - ter Wri - ter,   why don't you tell it

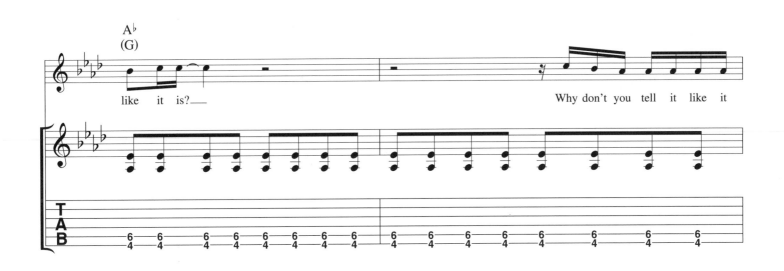

like it is?——   Why don't you tell it like it

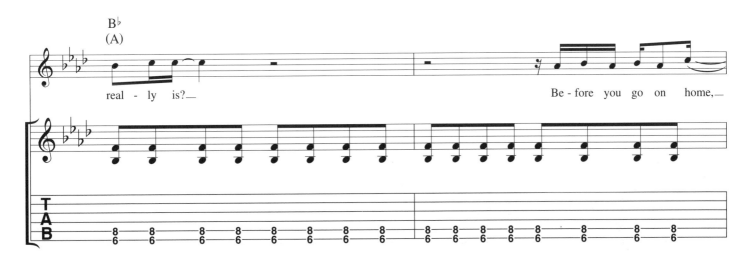

real - ly is?——   Be - fore you go on home,—

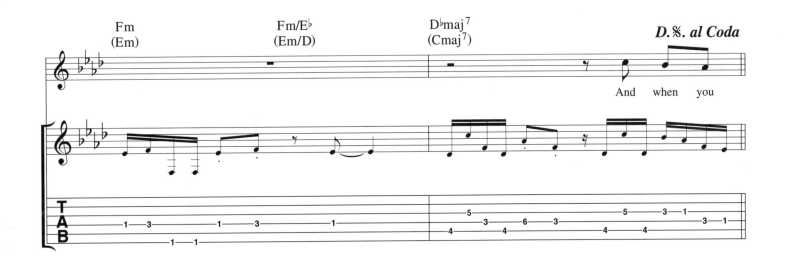

Coda

Chorus

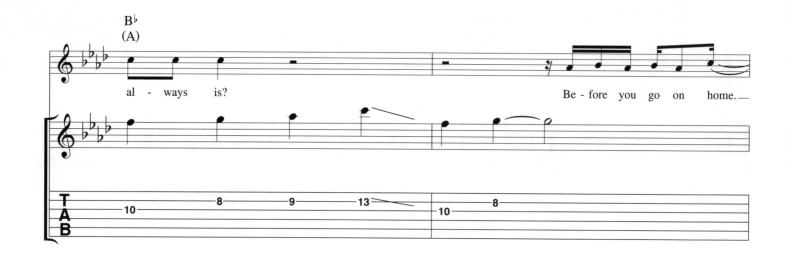

al - ways is?   Be - fore you go on home.—

1. D♭
(C)

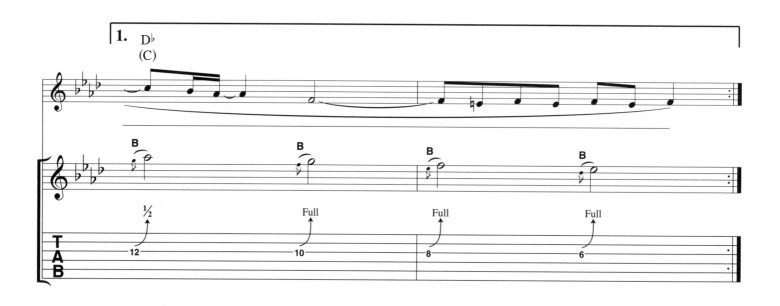

2.

D♭
(C)

home.—

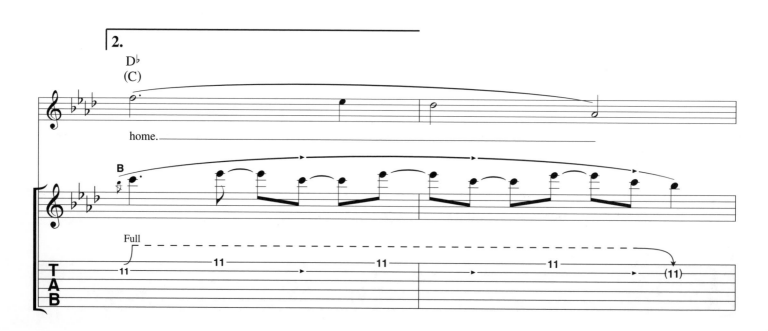

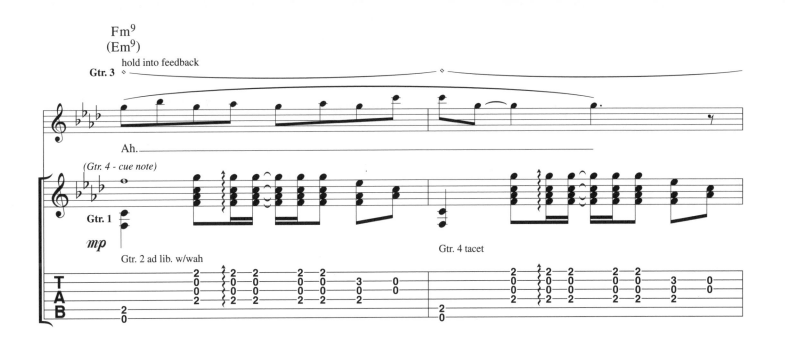

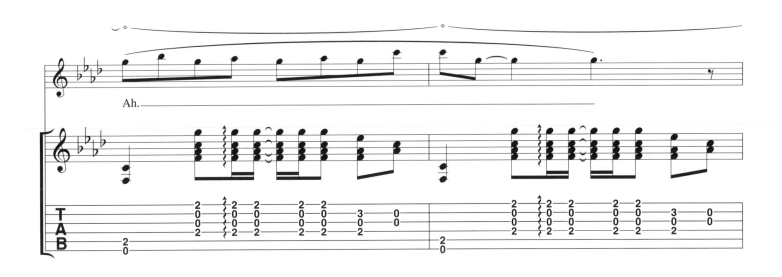

Step On My Old Size Nines

Words & Music by Kelly Jones

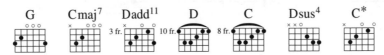

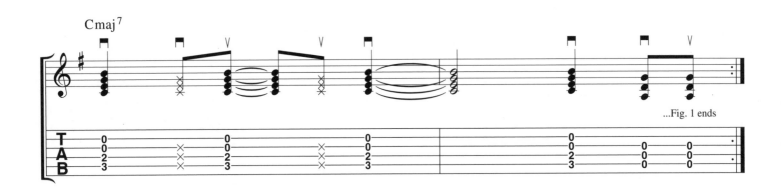

I'd like to know what it's all a-bout,_____
I'd like to know what you're all a-bout,_____

(Verse 3 see block lyric)

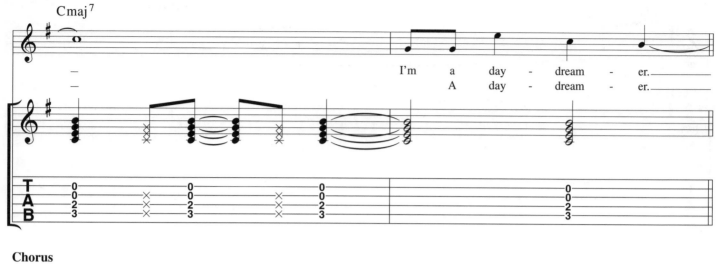

Cmaj⁷ ... I'm a day - dream - er. / A day - dream - er.

Chorus

Dadd¹¹ ... Then I watch the old ___ cou - ple
3°(%) Gtr. 2 w/Fig. 3 ... P.M.- - - - -

To Coda ⊕

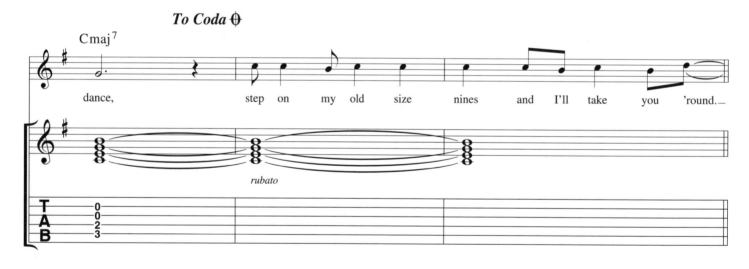

Cmaj⁷ ... dance, step on my old size nines and I'll take you 'round.—
rubato

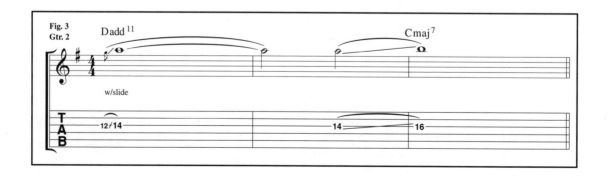

Fig. 3
Gtr. 2 Dadd¹¹ ... Cmaj⁷
w/slide
12/14 ... 14 16

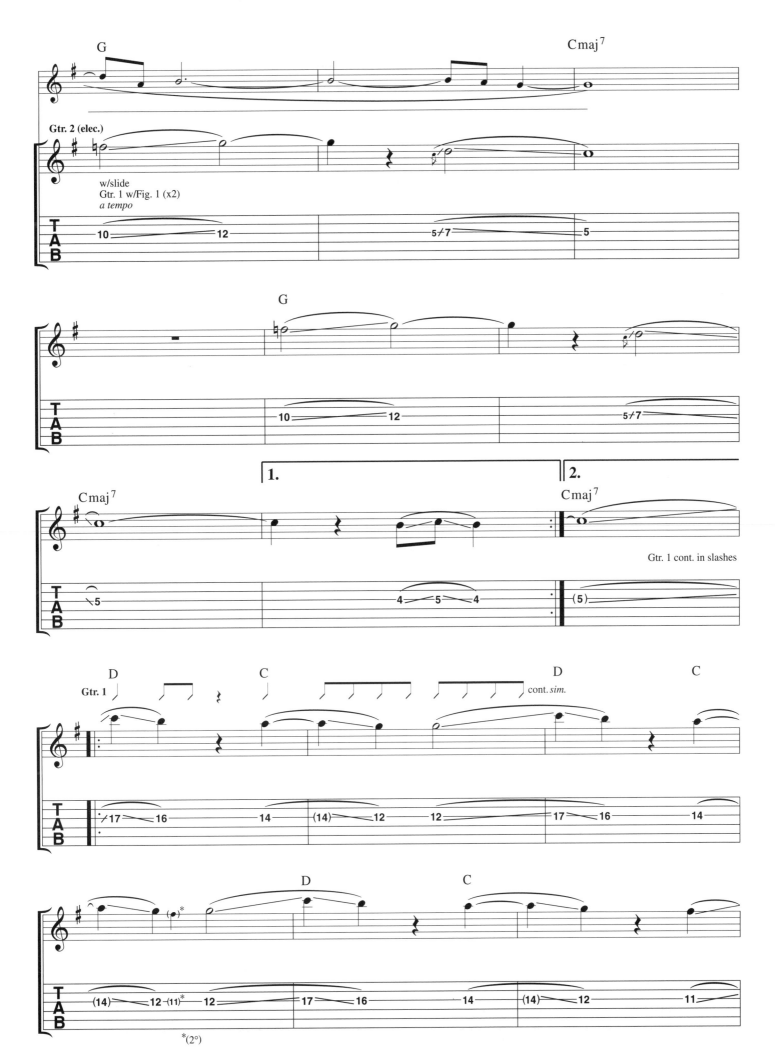

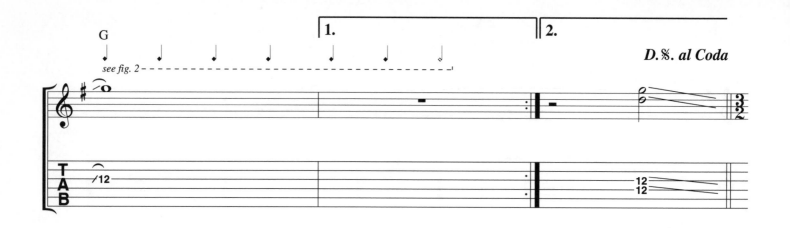

D.%. al Coda

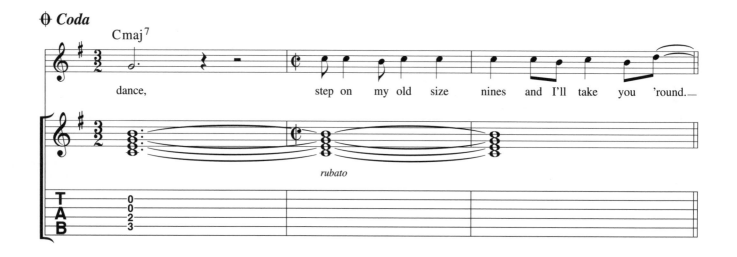

Coda

dance,   step on   my   old   size   nines   and I'll   take   you   'round.——

rubato

a tempo

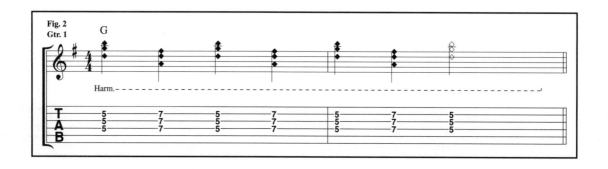

Fig. 2
Gtr. 1

Harm.--------

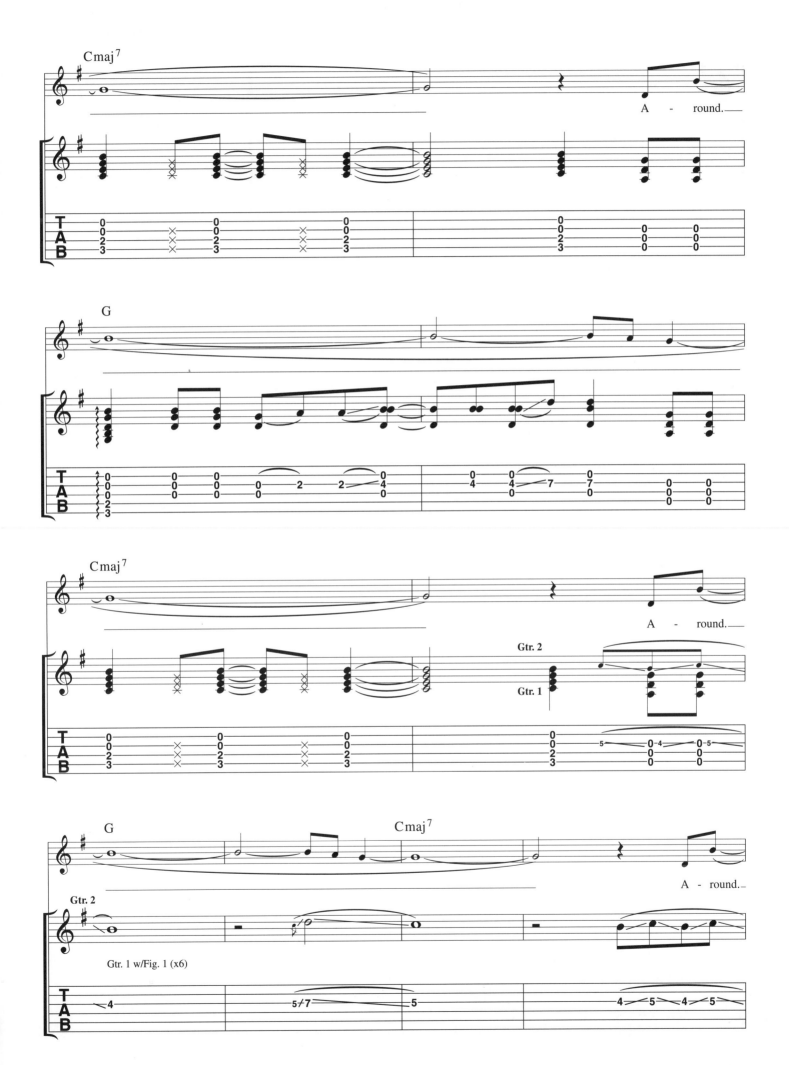

Verse 3:

I'd love to know what we're all about, we all have done
Am I gonna get old and laugh with someone?
Think I'll get me a boy and a girl, or not either?
Will I get what I want from this world?
I'm a daydreamer.

Then I watched the old couple dance (etc.)

Have A Nice Day

Words & Music by Kelly Jones

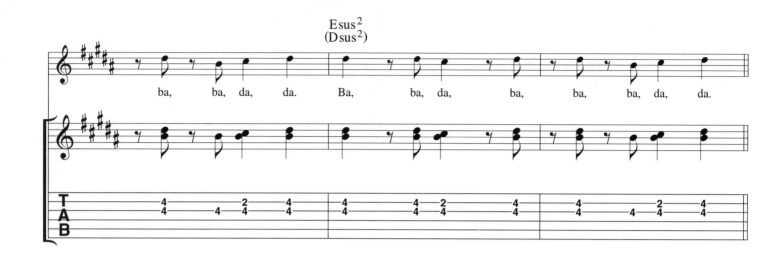

ba, ba, da, da. Ba, ba, da, ba, ba, ba, da, da.

Verse

1. San Fran - cis - co Bay past pier thir - ty nine, ear - ly P. M. can't

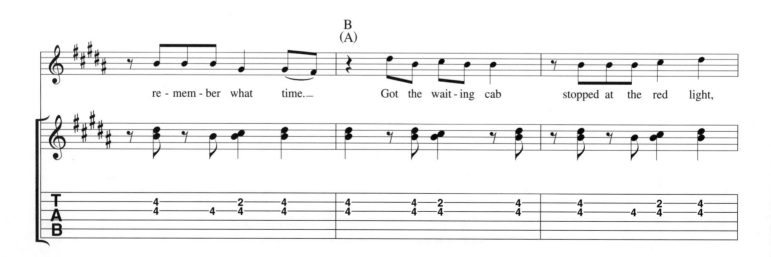

re - mem - ber what time.__ Got the wait - ing cab stopped at the red light,

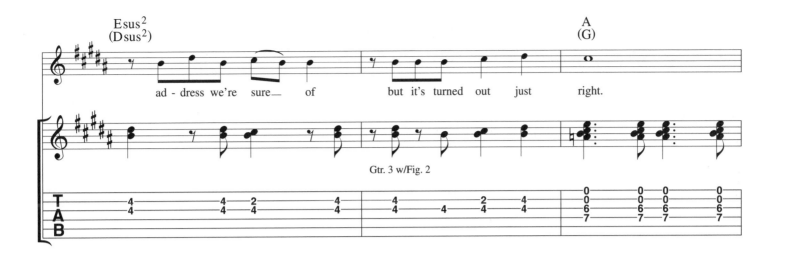

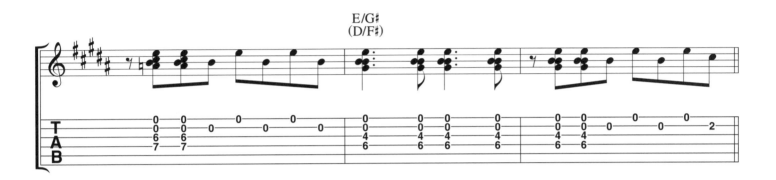

Verse %

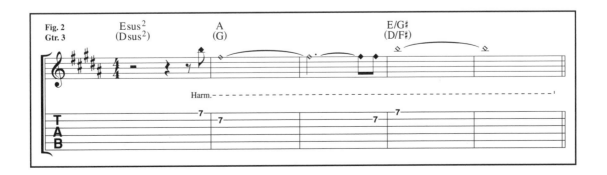

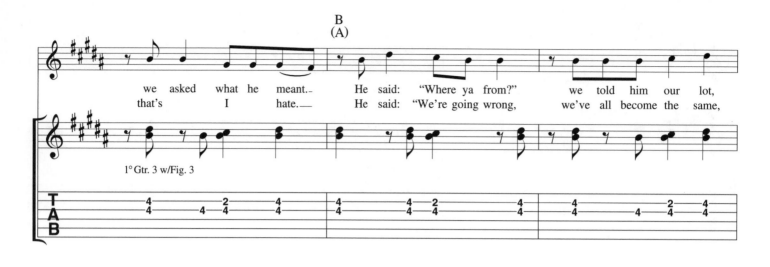

B
(A)

we asked what he meant.. He said: "Where ya from?" we told him our lot,
that's I hate.— He said: "We're going wrong, we've all become the same,

1° Gtr. 3 w/Fig. 3

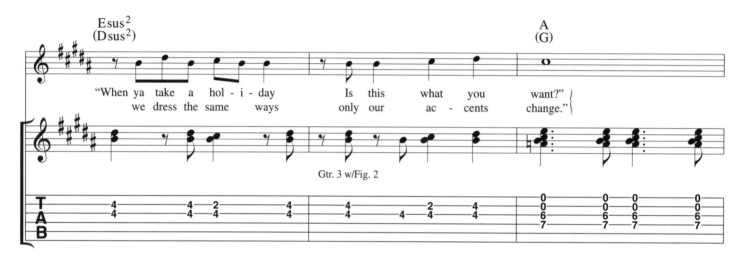

Esus²
(Dsus²)

A
(G)

"When ya take a hol-i-day Is this what you want?"
we dress the same ways only our ac-cents change."

Gtr. 3 w/Fig. 2

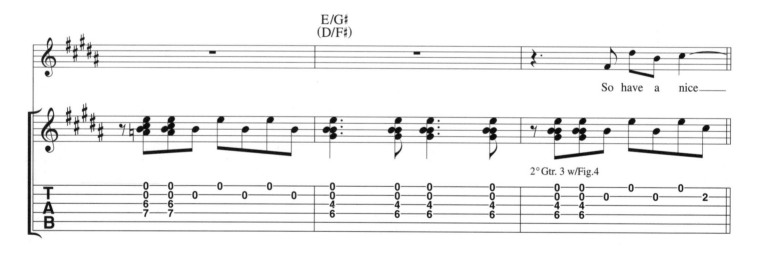

E/G♯
(D/F♯)

So have a nice——

2° Gtr. 3 w/Fig.4

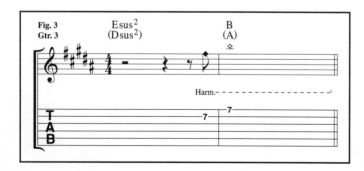

Fig. 3
Gtr. 3

Esus²
(Dsus²)

B
(A)

Harm.- - - - - - - - - - - - - -

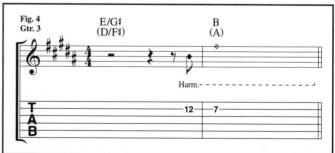

Fig. 4
Gtr. 3

E/G♯
(D/F♯)

B
(A)

Harm.- - - - - - - - - - - - - -

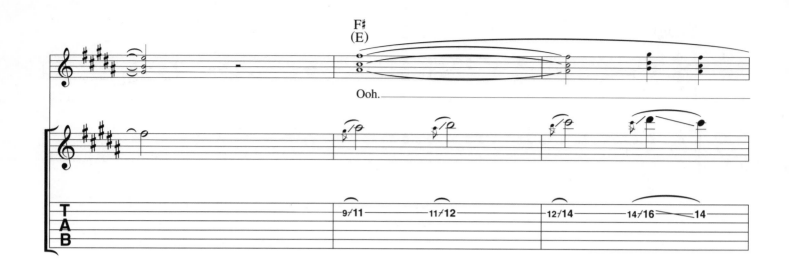

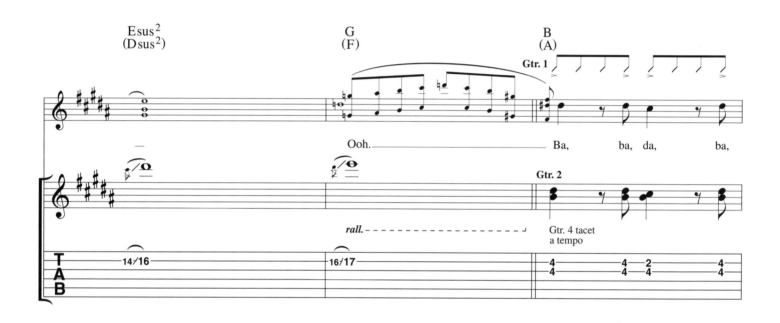

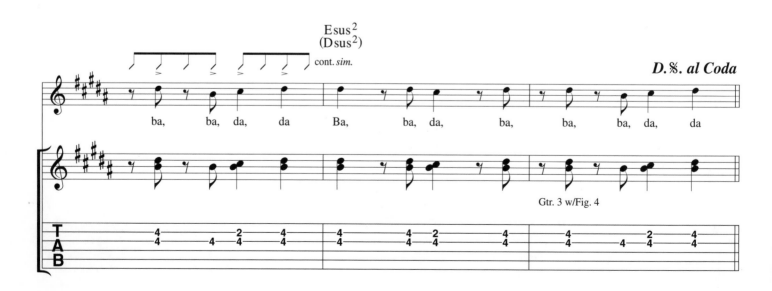

Verse 4:
Swim in the ocean
That be my dish
I drive around all day
And kill processed fish.
It's all money gum
No artists anymore
You're only in it now
To make more, more, more.
So have a nice day (etc.)

Nice To Be Out

Words & Music by Kelly Jones

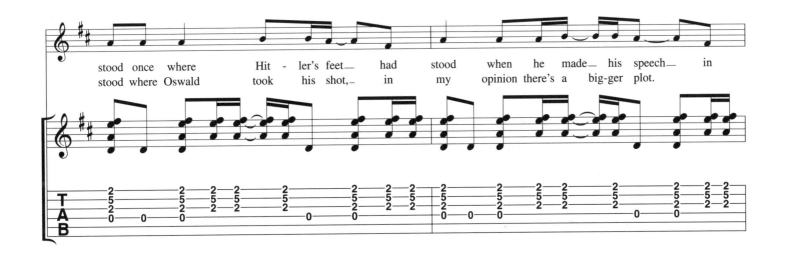

stood once where Hit - ler's feet__ had stood when he made_ his speech_ in
stood where Oswald took his shot,_ in my opinion there's a big-ger plot.

A⁵

Nur - em - burg in thir - ty eight,_ he tried to build__ the per - fect race,_ he said
Cost - ner's back and to the left, the pi - cket fence__ the bet - ter bet,__

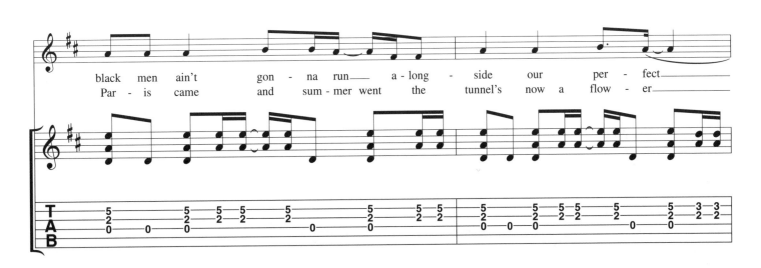

black men ain't gon - na run__ a - long - side our per - fect__
Par - is came and sum - mer went the tunnel's now a flow - er__

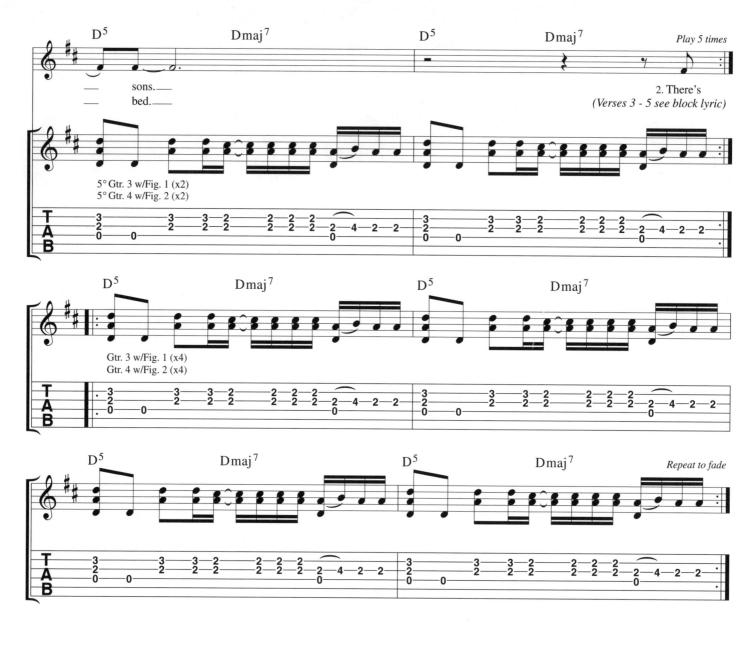

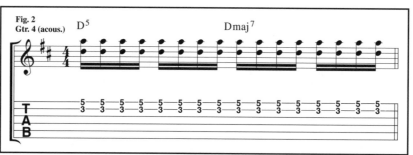

Verse 3:

The famous turf that made Geoff Hurst
The vodka stops to quench my thirst
The Golden Gate stroke Alcatraz
And the fat man failed to get us passes
Jimmy's corner in Raging Bull
De Niro's jokes and bottled Pills
Elvis tales from Mr Woodward
Any Richard Burton if you could.

Verse 4:

Tourists stare at tourist stops
One more picture, one more god
Another top up for a change
It makes you think, it makes you sane
Talking more about yourself
There's a mirror too, have a check
Cheques are always passing through
Some depart but a lot come too.

Verse 5:

Restaurant talk or pick your teeth
You bite your tongue or chew your meat
Sleep or drink or drink to sleep
And one more week and we will meet
Talk of what we haven't done
Since we departed back a month
We argue why we have to shout
All in all it's nice to be out.

Watch Them Fly Sundays

Words & Music by Kelly Jones

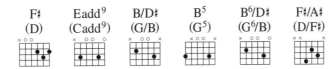

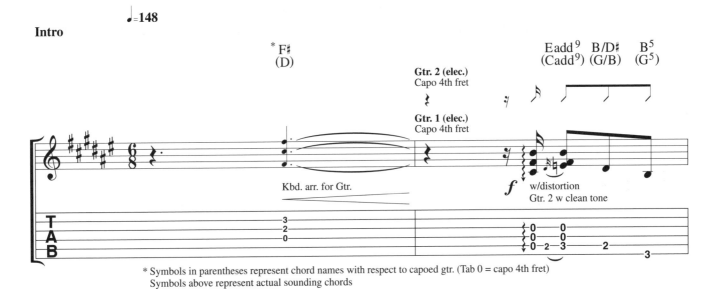

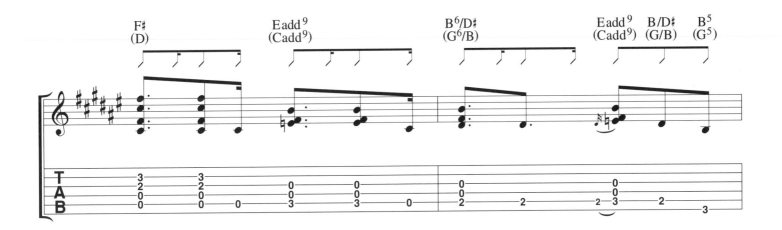

* Symbols in parentheses represent chord names with respect to capoed gtr. (Tab 0 = capo 4th fret)
Symbols above represent actual sounding chords

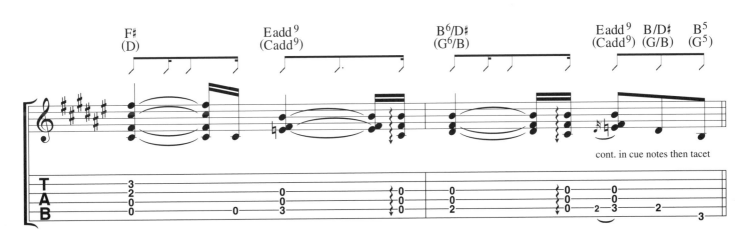

Verse

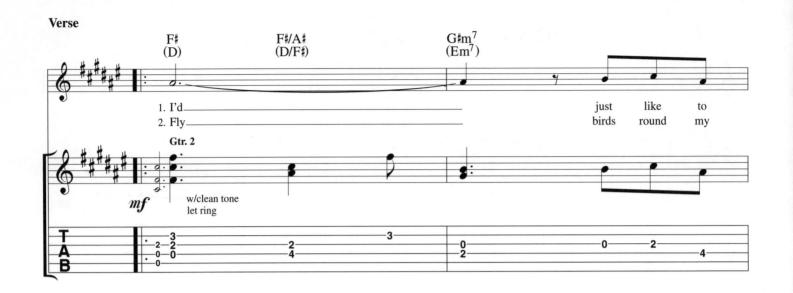

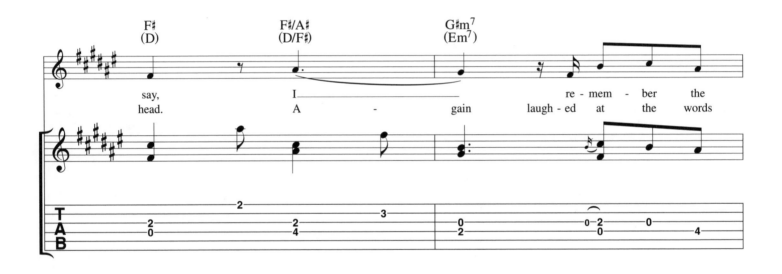

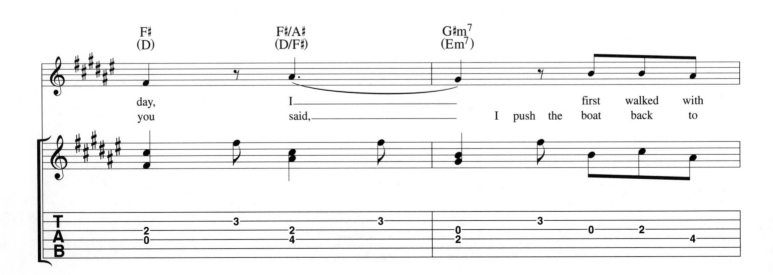

46

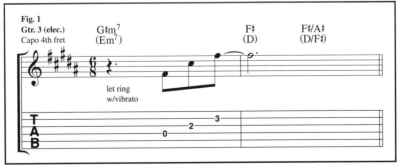

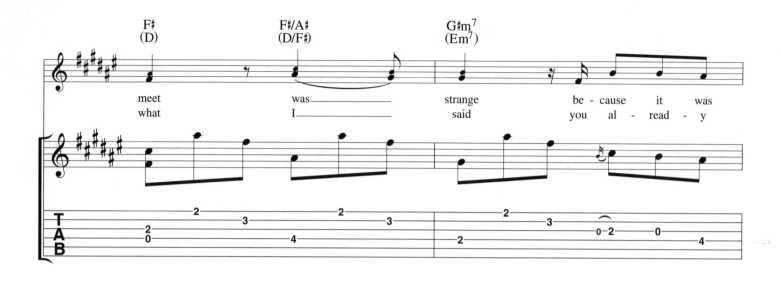

meet   was_____   strange   be - cause   it   was

what   I_____   said   you   al - read - y

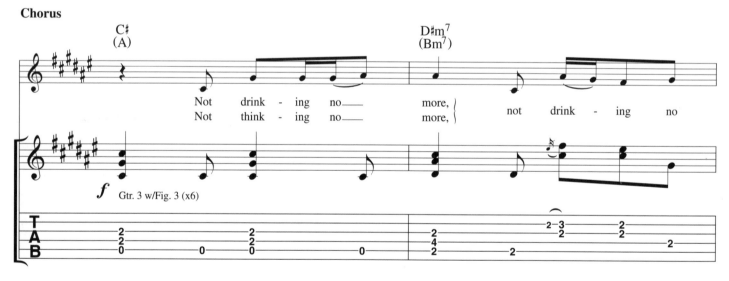

new._____

knew._____

2° Gtrs. 1+2 w/Fig. 2

1° w/Gtr. 1
Gtrs. 1+2 w/dist.

Chorus

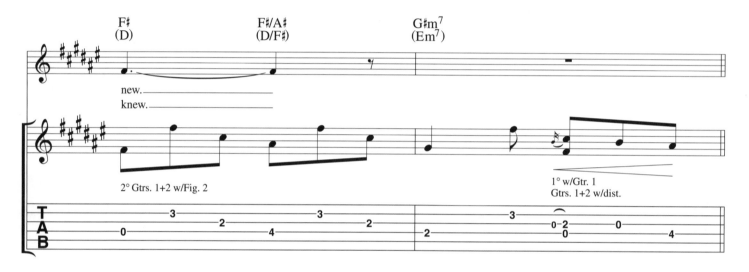

Not   drink - ing   no_____ more,   not   drink - ing   no

Not   think - ing   no_____ more,

Gtr. 3 w/Fig. 3 (x6)

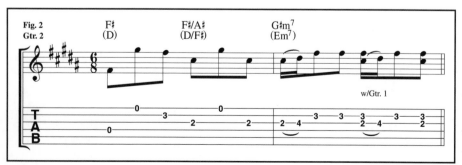

w/Gtr. 1

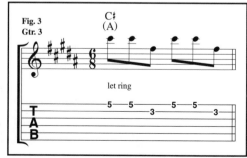

let ring

48

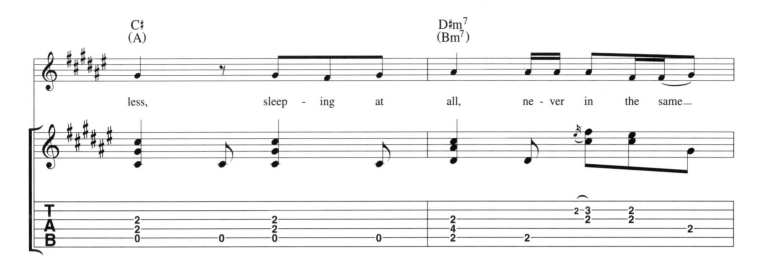

less,   sleep - ing   at   all,   ne - ver   in   the   same —

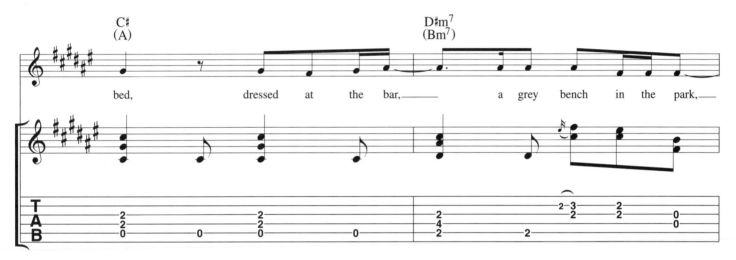

bed,   dressed   at   the   bar, —   a   grey   bench   in   the   park, —

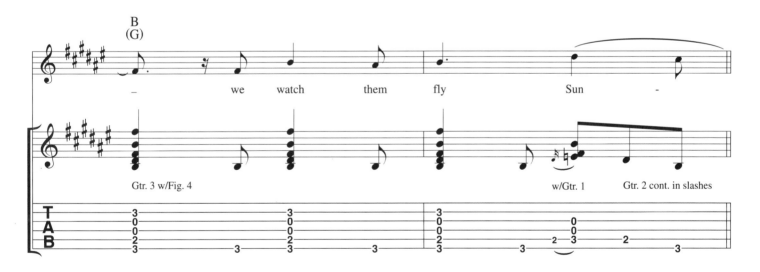

— we   watch   them   fly   Sun -

Gtr. 3 w/Fig. 4   w/Gtr. 1   Gtr. 2 cont. in slashes

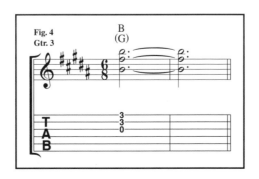

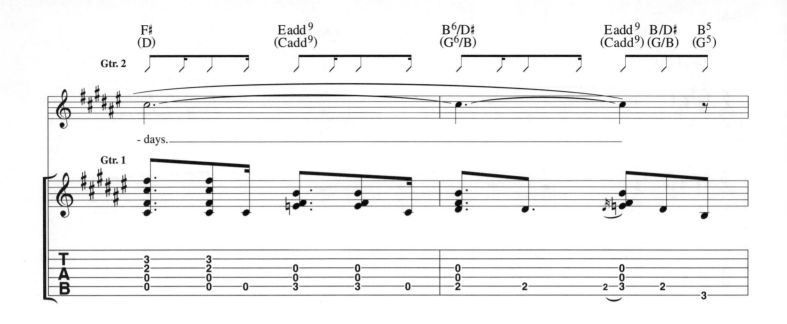

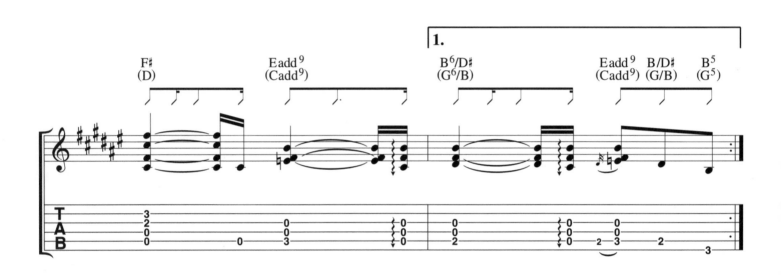

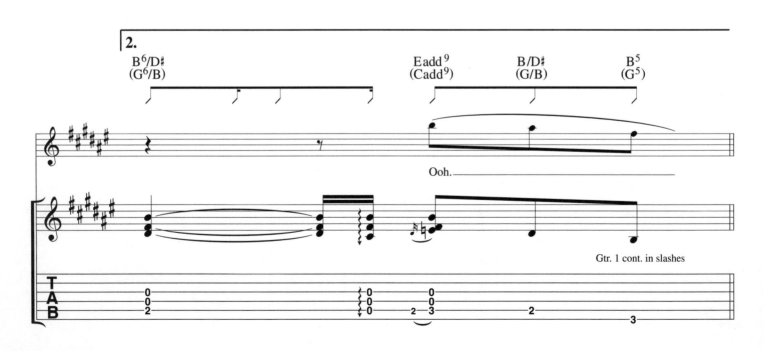

Solo

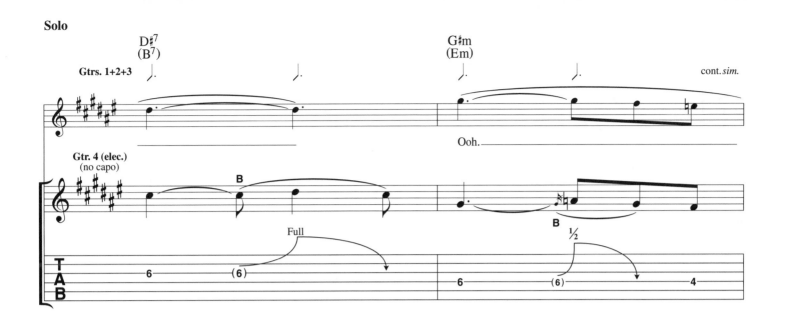

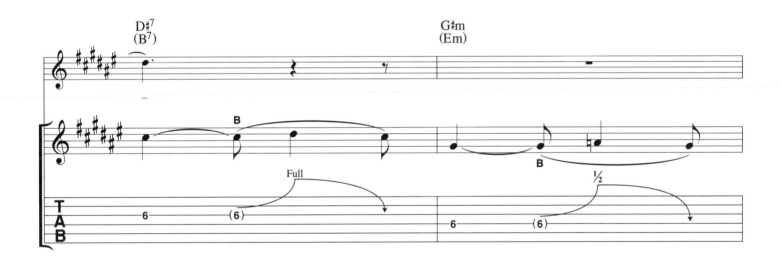

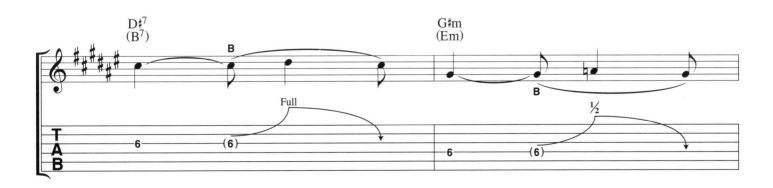

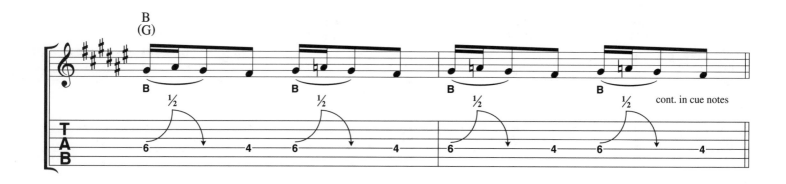

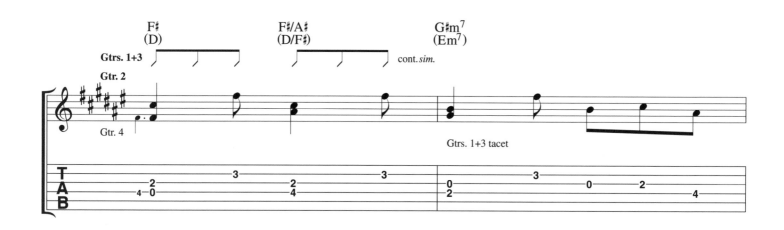

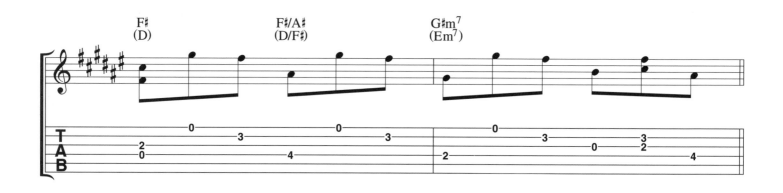

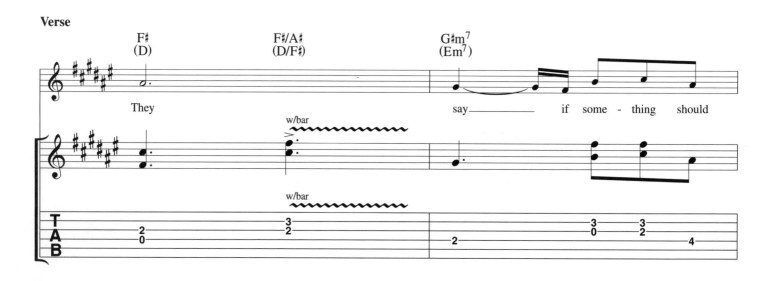

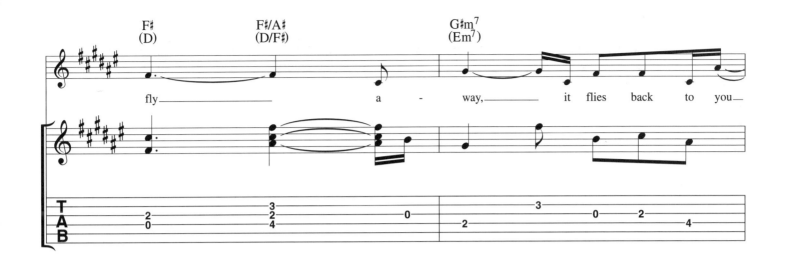

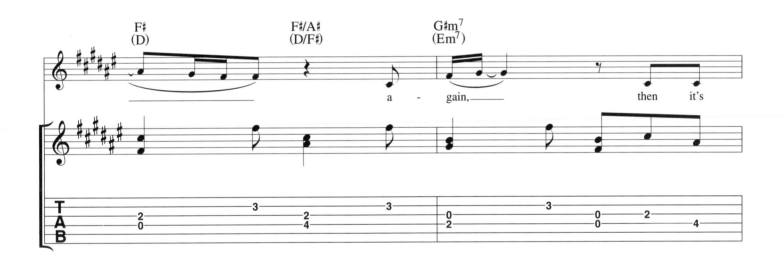

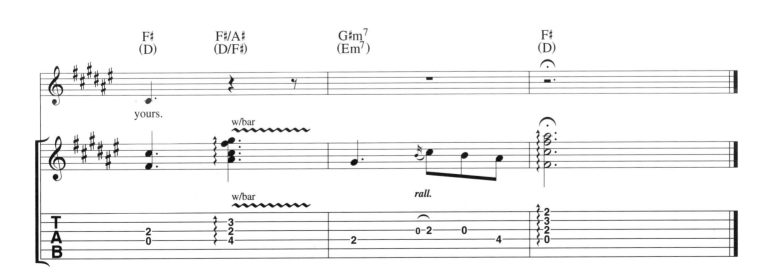

Everyday I Think Of Money

Words & Music by Kelly Jones

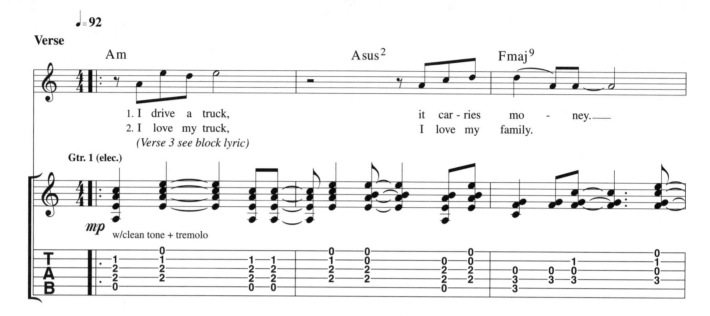

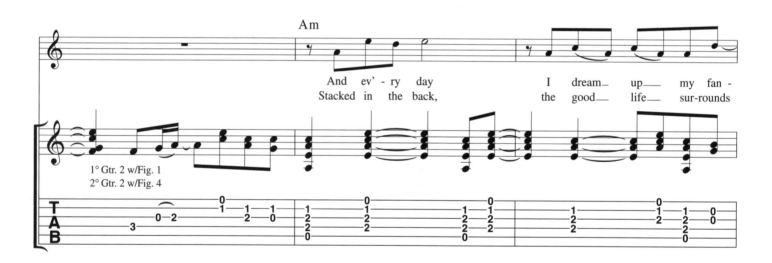

1. I drive a truck, it car-ries mo-ney.
2. I love my truck, I love my family.
(Verse 3 see block lyric)

And ev'-ry day I dream up my fan-
Stacked in the back, the good life sur-rounds

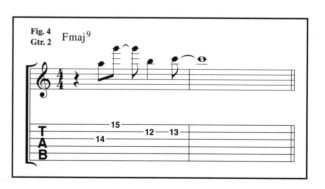

Chorus

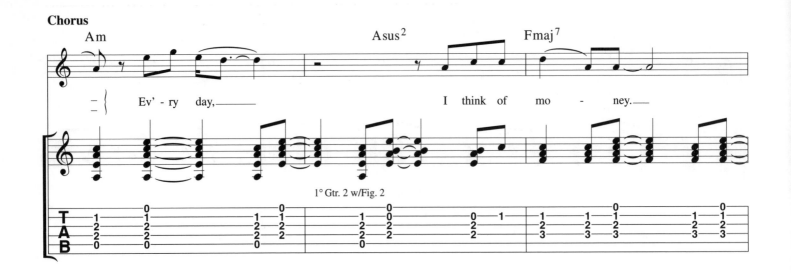

Ev'-ry day,_____ I think of mo — ney.___

1° Gtr. 2 w/Fig. 2

To Coda ⊕

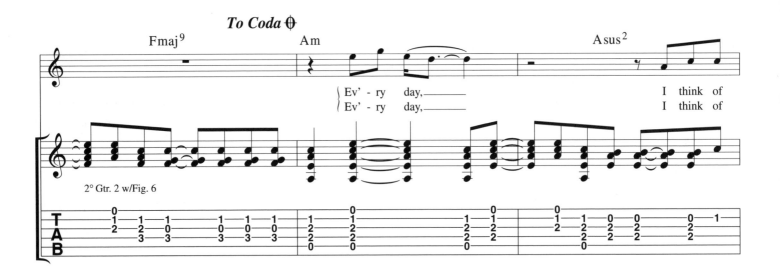

Ev'-ry day,_____ I think of
Ev'-ry day,_____ I think of

2° Gtr. 2 w/Fig. 6

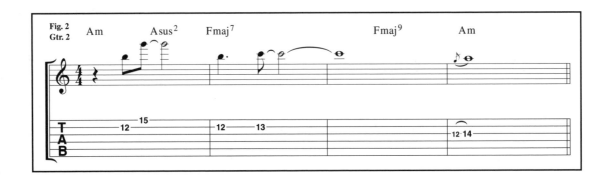

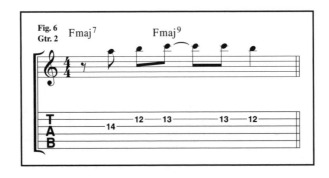

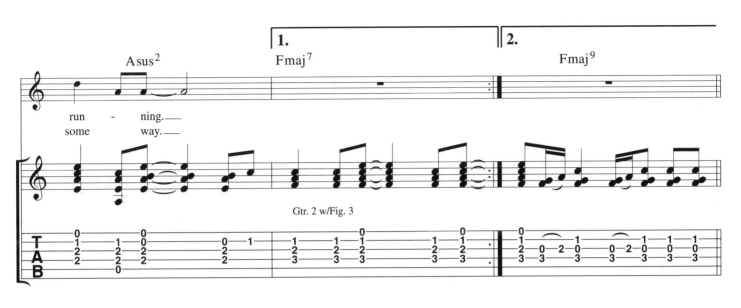

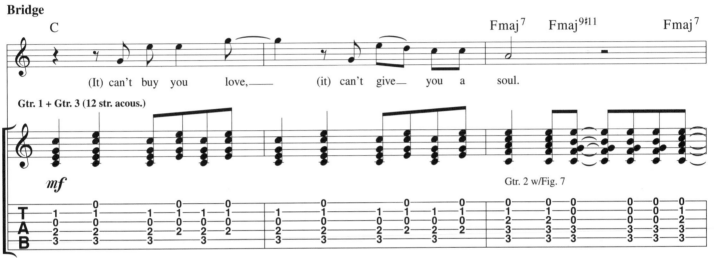

Bridge

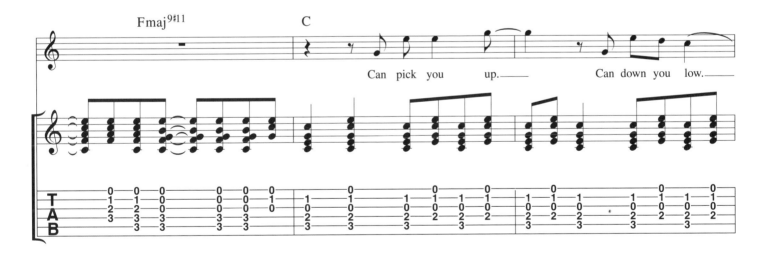

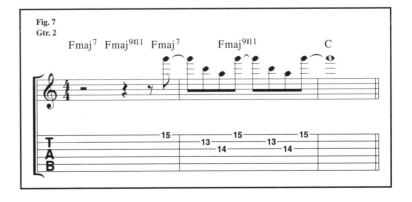

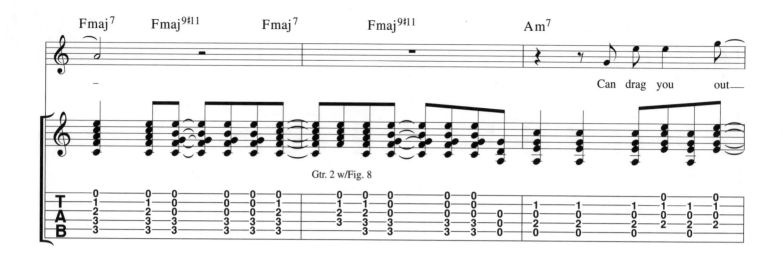

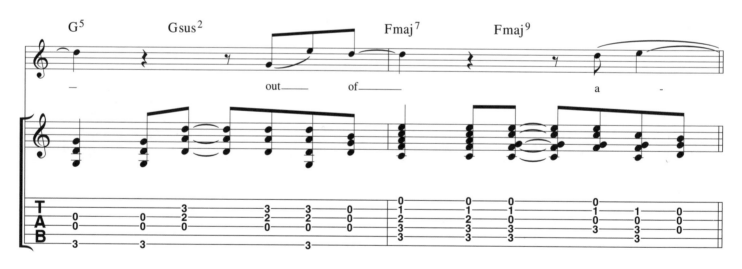

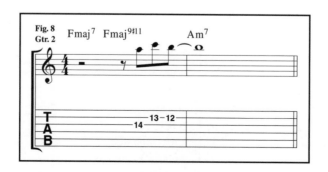

D.C. al Coda

Ev' - ry day,_____ I miss my fam' - ly._____

Verse 3:
Sat in a truck
It carries convicts
My hands are bound
To the seat by hand cuffs.

Tomorrow I'll maybe
Walk around the yard
Or paint in my cell
And hate imprisonment
Every day I think of money
Every day I miss my family.

Maybe

Words & Music by Kelly Jones

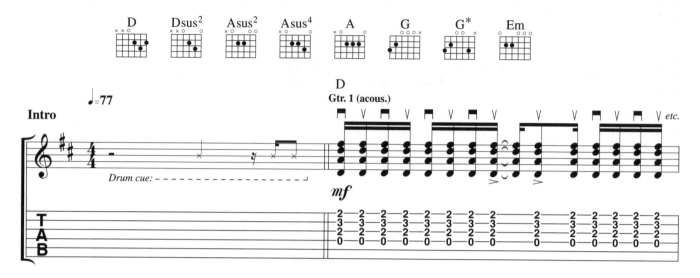

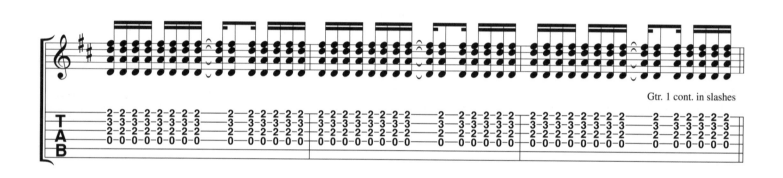

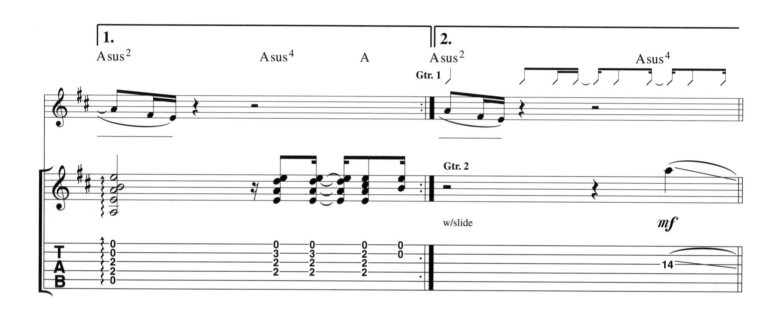

Bridge

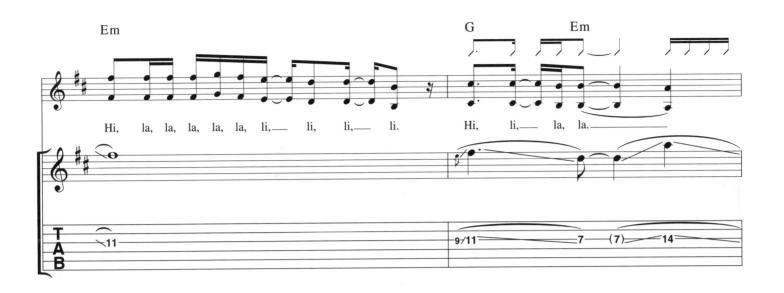

Hi, la, la, la, la, la, li,— li, li,— li. Hi, li,— la, la.—

Hi, la, la, la, la, la, li,— li, li,— li. Hi, la, la, la, la, la, li,— li, li.—

cont. sim.

Hi, la, la, la, la, la, li,— li, li,— li. Hi, li,— la, la.—

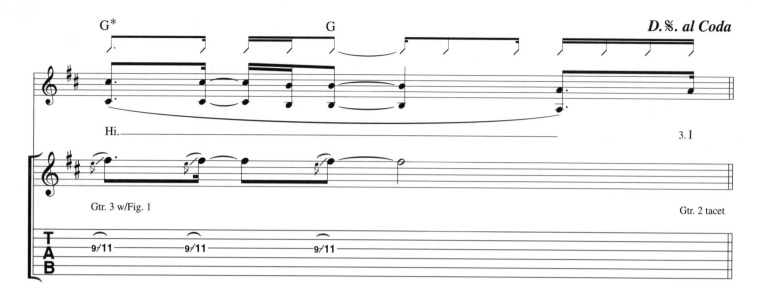

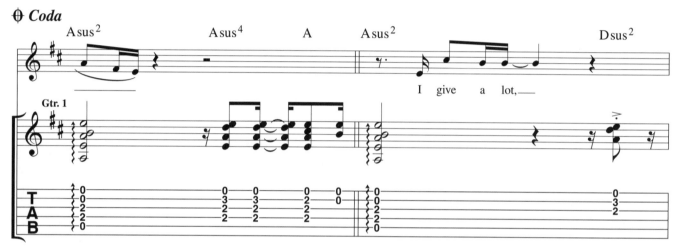

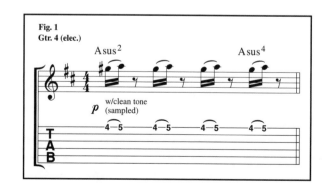

Fig. 1
Gtr. 4 (elec.)

Asus² Asus⁴

w/clean tone
(sampled)

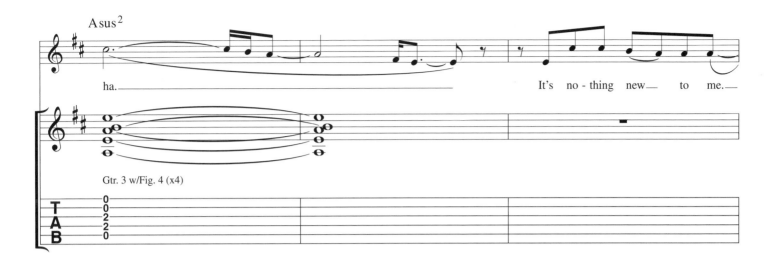

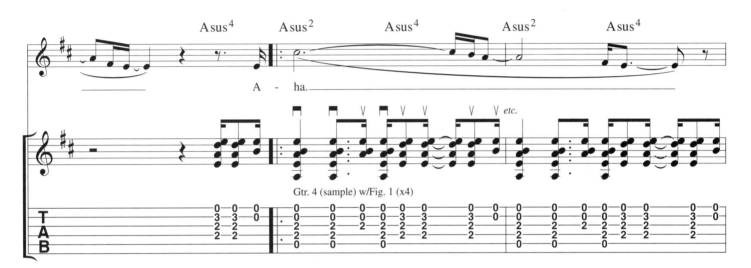

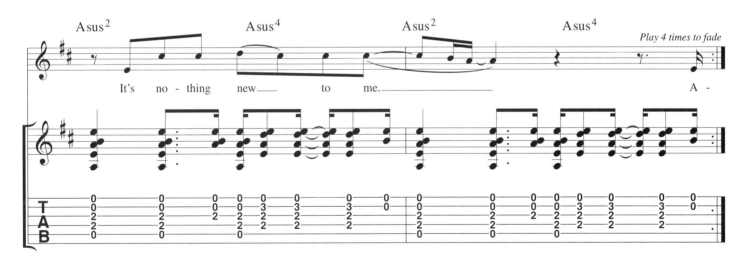

Verse 3:

May be laughing
Something lacking
Always sometimes
All I hear is how it's meant to
be.

Maybe learning
Always searching
I keep asking
Things I'll know too soon
Things I'll know too soon.

Chorus:

We talk a lot
Don't do a lot
It's nothing new to me.

Caravan Holiday

Words & Music by Kelly Jones

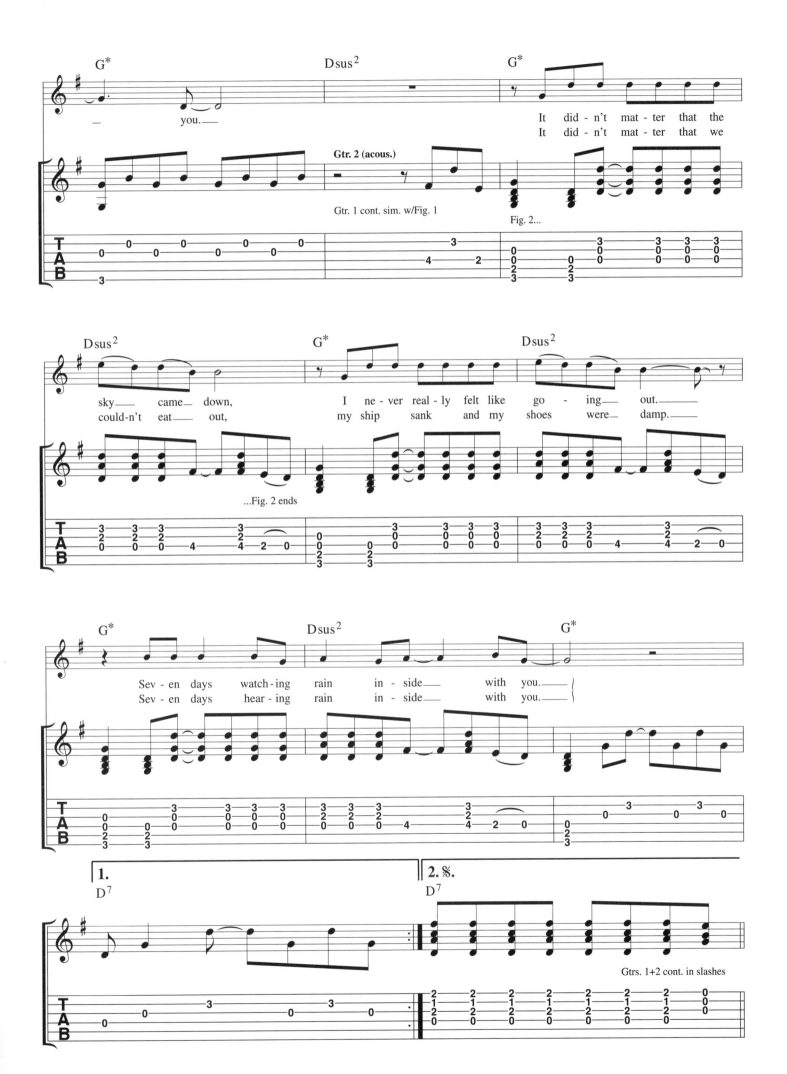

⊕ Coda

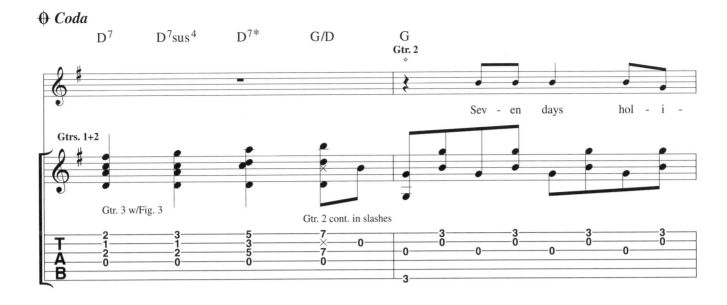

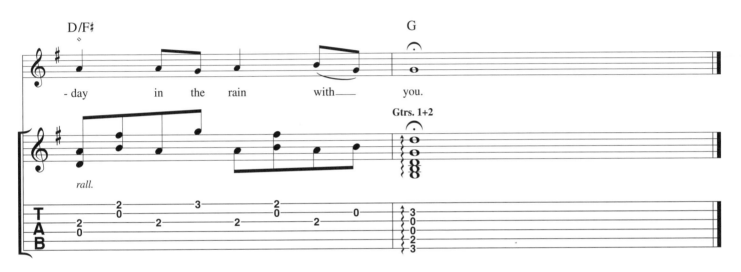

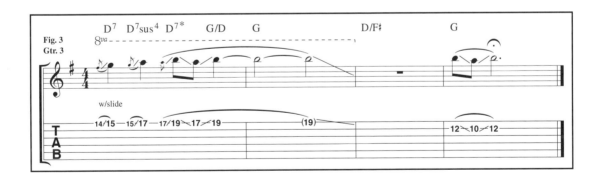

Verse 3:
Lie awake drinking late is all that's left to do
Not a sound but the rain on the pale blue roof
It didn't matter that we couldn't sleep out
I never really felt like sleeping rough
Seven day holiday drinking dry with you.

Rooftop

Words & Music by Kelly Jones

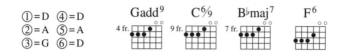

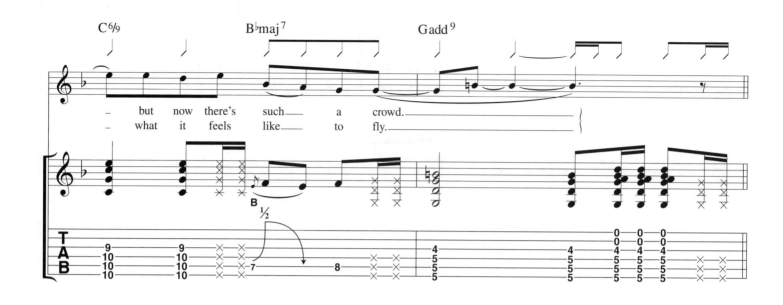

Chorus

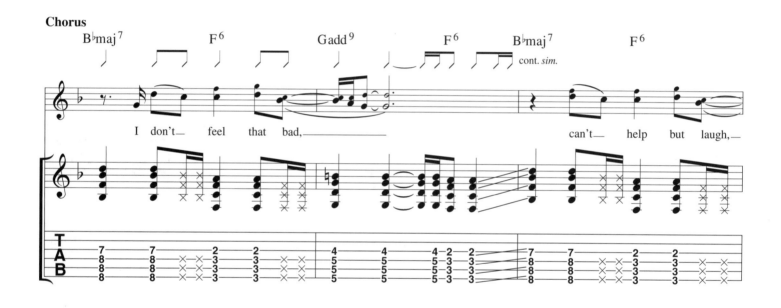

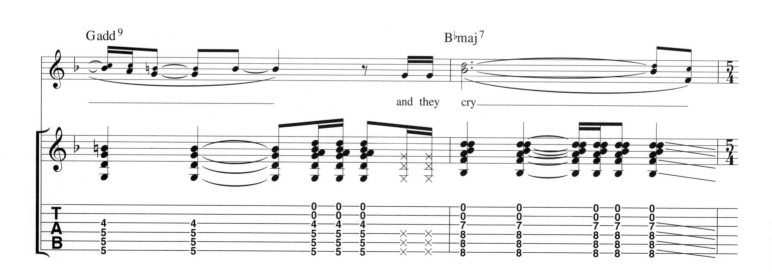

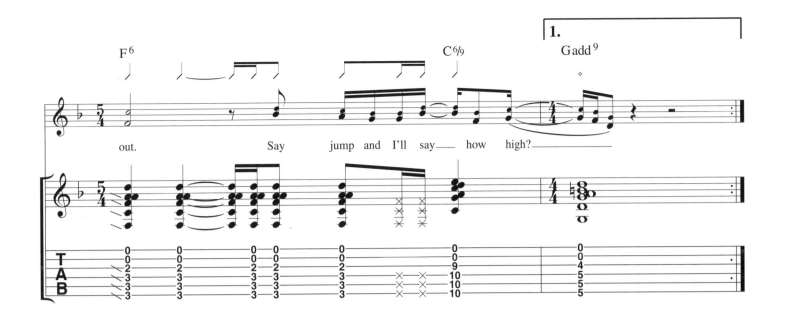

1.

F6 ... C6/9 ... Gadd9

out. Say jump and I'll say— how high?

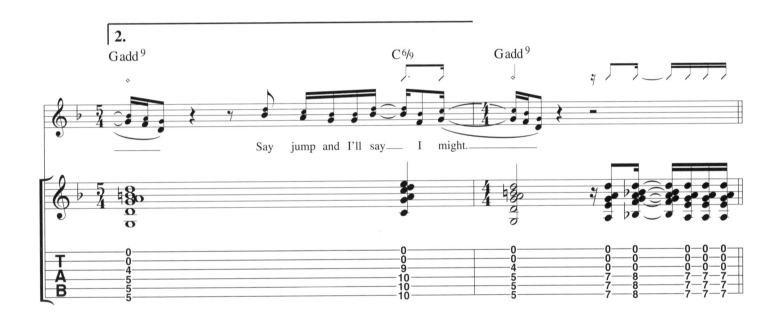

2.

Gadd9 ... C6/9 ... Gadd9

Say jump and I'll say— I might.

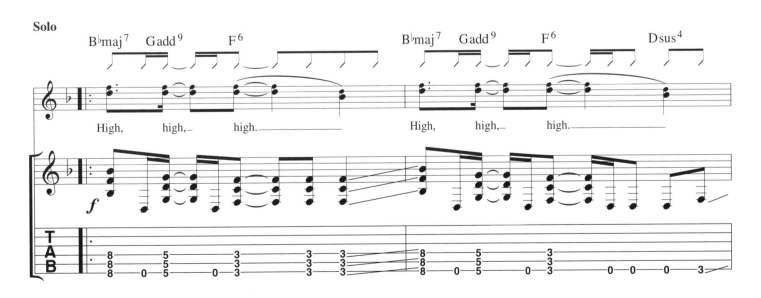

Solo

B♭maj7 Gadd9 F6 ... B♭maj7 Gadd9 F6 ... Dsus4

High, high,— high. High, high,— high.

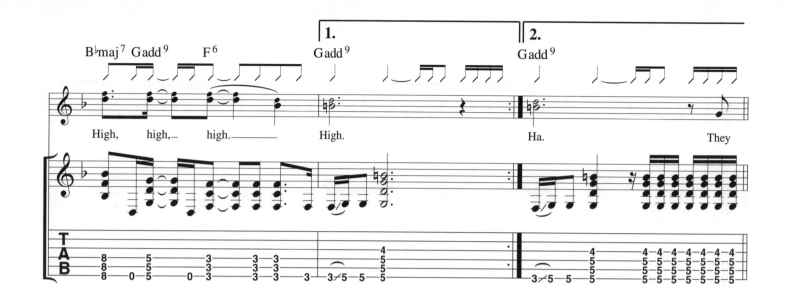

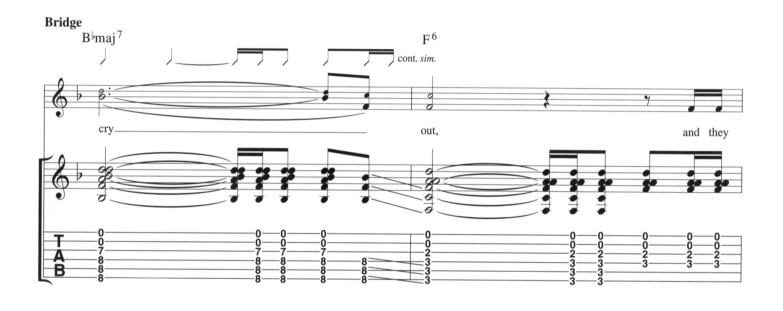

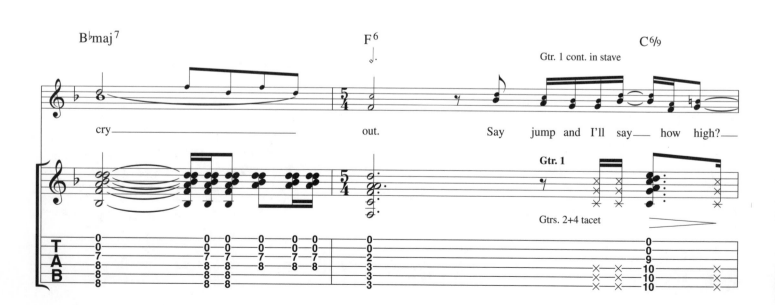

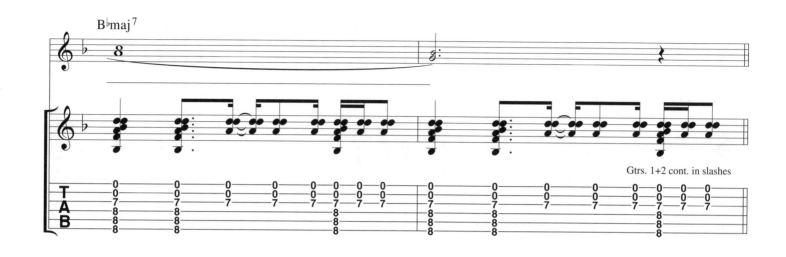

Gtrs. 1+2 cont. in slashes

Outro

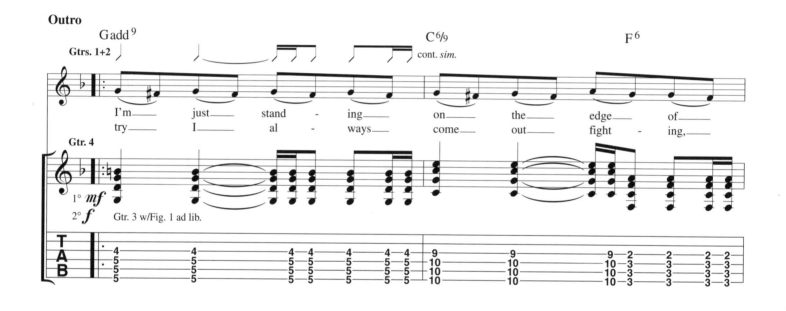

I'm—— just—— stand - ing—— on—— the—— edge—— of——
try—— I—— al - ways—— come—— out—— fight - ing,——

Gtr. 3 w/Fig. 1 ad lib.

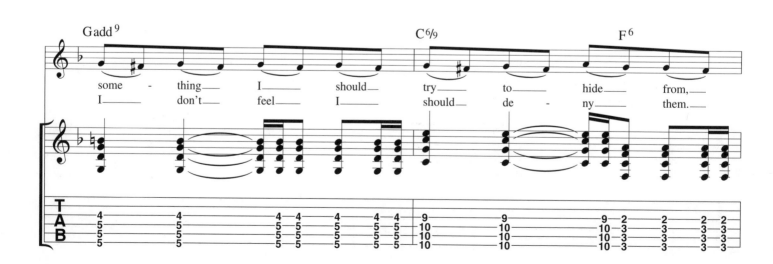

some - thing—— I—— should—— try—— to—— hide—— from,——
I—— don't—— feel—— I—— should—— de - ny—— them.——

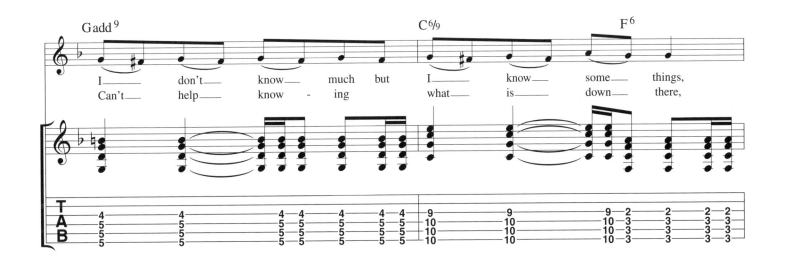

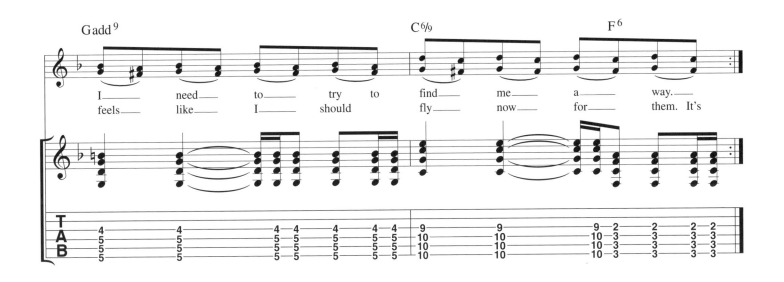

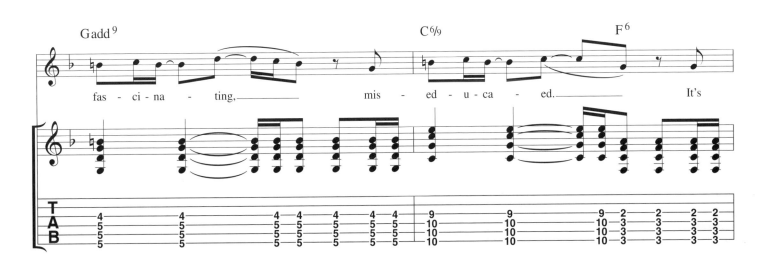

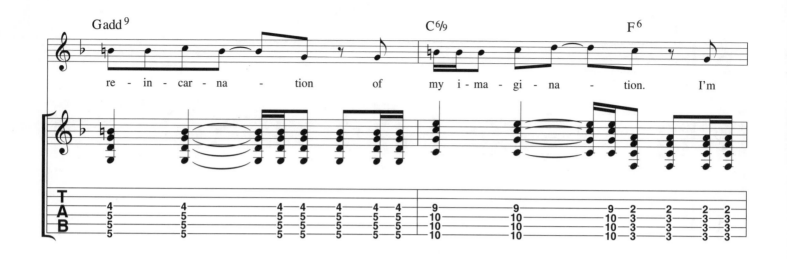

re - in - car - na - tion of my i - ma - gi - na - tion. I'm

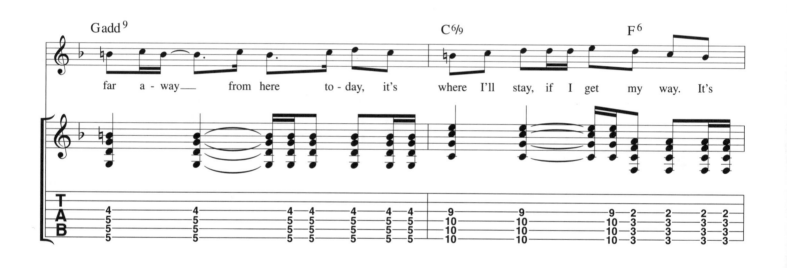

far a - way___ from here to - day, it's where I'll stay, if I get my way. It's

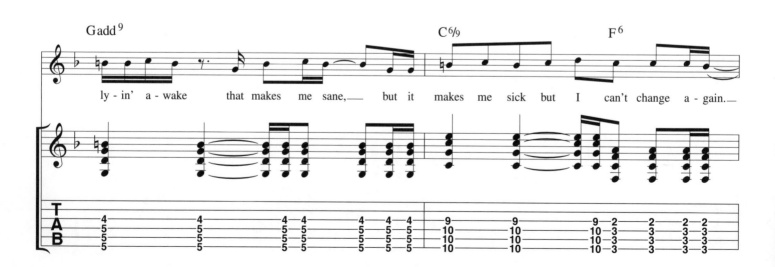

ly - in' a - wake that makes me sane,___ but it makes me sick but I can't change a - gain.___

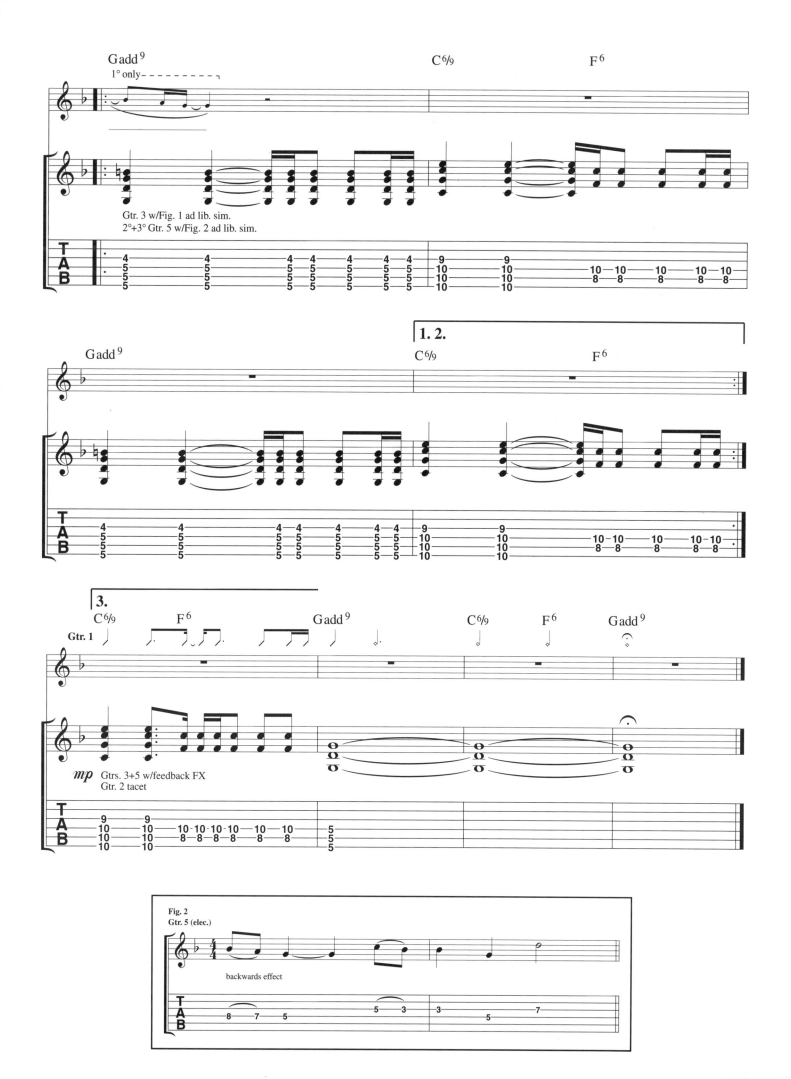

12/01 (42320)

Exclusive distributors:

Music Sales Limited

8/9 Frith Street, London W1V 5TZ, England.

Music Sales Pty Limited

120 Rothschild Avenue, Rosebery, NSW 2018, Australia.

Order No.AM970530

ISBN 0-7119-8875-7

Music arranged by Matt Cowe.

Music engraved by Digital Music Art.

Artwork courtesy of V2 Records.

Printed in the United Kingdom by Caligraving Limited, Thetford, Norfolk.

Your Guarantee of Quality:

As publishers, we strive to produce every book to the highest commercial standards.

The music has been freshly engraved and, whilst endeavouring to retain the

original running order of the recorded album, the book has been carefully designed

to minimise awkward page turns and to make playing from it a real pleasure.

Particular care has been given to specifying acid-free, neutral-sized

paper made from pulps which have not been elemental chlorine bleached.

This pulp is from farmed sustainable forests and was produced with special regard for the environment.

Throughout, the printing and binding have been planned to ensure a sturdy,

attractive publication which should give years of enjoyment.

If your copy fails to meet our high standards, please inform us and we will gladly replace it.

Music Sales' complete catalogue describes thousands of titles and is

available in full colour sections by subject, direct from Music Sales Limited.

Please state your areas of interest and send a cheque/postal order for £1.50 for postage to:

Music Sales Limited, Newmarket Road, Bury St. Edmunds, Suffolk IP33 3YB.

www.musicsales.com